Thinking About Quitting Medicine, Volume 2

Swiner Publishing Co.

Table of Contents

Introduction

It feels so good to be back here!

Your response to Volume 1 was out of this world. From showing up to support our visionary physician authors across platforms to showing up at the book launches in Atlanta and Durham, you have let us know that we are tuning in to your frequency. You are Thinking About Quitting Medicine and you are ready to do more than bellyache about it. You yearn to feel alive and passionate and in love with each new day again. You long to feel that sense of pride after each task completed as it feels connected to your higher purpose.

You want that feeling of fulfillment that is spreading through the internet world, but you can't seem to figure out how to manifest that in this life, this hospital, this clinic, this call room, this phone call, this procedure. Maybe you're bogged down from the new EMR with each hospital administration change. Maybe you're over the 18-year-old-sounding snarky insurance guy that you get to talk to before you work your way up the chain of command. It shouldn't bother you as much as it does. It's a little thing added on to so many other little things and it feels like death by a thousand cuts.

In numbing the stress of the day grind out you may have shut out your emotions and somewhere along the journey forgotten how to turn them back on.

This is the place where the culture and media will throw around phrases like imposter syndrome, emotional exhaustion, burnout, stress-induced executive dysfunction and roll out charts and checklists.

This is not that book. Our physicians dug deep and found the courage to tell their stories and serve as their contribution to the world. Sure, they may pepper the above phrases into their lives here and there, these phenomena are real and there is no denying the physician suicide crisis.

In this book we bring you a reminder that there are other ways to interpret your current situation with an eye on the possibilities. Each physician-author's deeply moving vignette takes you through what they felt that led them to think about quitting medicine. In each journey, you'll discover that despite fears similar to yours, setbacks, trials, and tribulations, they chose to continue to believe. They chose to continue to imagine and to walk in their purpose.

We welcome you to volume two. We invite you to join our authors on the Thinking About Quitting Medicine page where you can continue to build a deeper relationship with each of them. Come share your story with our docs so they can help you see what's possible for you.

Thank you once again for your continued support.

Nicole and Mani

Foreword

The only thing harder than committing to a career in medicine, is deciding to step away from it.

Not only have you dedicated your life to this dynamic field that demands every waking moment of your being-- physically, emotionally and mentally; but so has every being who you have engaged with since your journey began.

Separating from this entity, from a traditional standpoint, or altogether, is nothing less than escaping the intense and overwhelming embrace of a jealous lover.

Your friends, family, colleagues and casual acquaintances will be completely devastated by the mere thought of you doing anything but being of service and available.

There is a stigma attached to this specialty; an almost moral authority or tag that is assigned to your being; and when you disengage from that persona there is a loss, not only for you, but for all of this around you.

So, to take on this journey of 'Thinking About Quitting Medicine' is not only an exercise in humility, introspection, self-care, growth and spiritual awakening, but also in forcing your world to take this amazing ride right along with you.

It's a doozy, but we know you can do it.

Take the journey along with me as we encounter the unique and self-reclaiming journey of seven brave Docs.

Let's take the current Doc as an example of what happens daily in the world of medicine.

Let's rewind the clock to when the proverbial fan was doused with unsaid post-digestive matter:

Subjective:
38-year-old practicing Plastic Surgeon, married with a ten-month-old baby, who has just days ago left a full-time

position as an employed physician. She never took a break and started working a full- time consultation practice, all while building a private practice, attending interviews for practice loans at night, trying to rent out the home she left in another city, all while still being a wife and mom. Sound overwhelming and exhausting? Yeah, so said her body which crashed and burned just as this was all going on.

Patient presents with vague, yet persistent neurological symptoms that eventually was diagnosed as a pretty significant first episode of relapsing, remitting type of Multiple Sclerosis (MS).

Objective:

On exam she is weathered, underweight and has neurological deficits consistent with the brain MRI scan findings. She has hit a clinical, emotional, spiritual and physical brick wall. She surrenders.

Assessment:

Chronic lack of self-care resulting in devastating and career-altering diagnosis.

Plan:

Options are to return to the same schedule and work as long and as hard until her body and soul run out; as so many other physicians around her have done and continue to do. The other option is to step back, take a breath and figure out a way to live and serve that places her as a priority, thereby being able to continue to serve as provider, mom, wife and every other hat that society has bestowed upon her.

Thankfully, she chose the latter.

To paraphrase Malcolm X, if you put kittens in an oven you cannot then call them muffins.

Likewise, with physicians, when you take us out of the traditional arena of medicine, its impact on our souls and beings is irrevocable and influences everything we do.

Our process, intent, duty, desire and motivation remain the same. We are of service. Our goals are to invoke life-long, indelible change on those who we embrace.

Now is the time to take those well-honed skills and incorporate them into an expanded vision that also includes care of ourselves; making us whole and well even while leaving an even greater impact than we thought possible.

--Lisa Whitty Bradley, MD

LaTosha Flowers, MD

"I want to be remembered as the doctor who treated my patients not only with medical knowledge, but also with common sense, caring and respect. For those thinking about quitting medicine, don't quit. Change your direction instead. Explore other pathways within medicine to apply your education, gifts, and talents."

L. Flowers, MD

Dr. Flowers is a family medicine physician. Her areas of expertise include urgent care, occupational care, hospice and palliative care and neuropathy. She is also very active in her community and working hard to make a difference with B.R.A.I.Ns & Beauty, a teen girl talk series. Aside from mentoring young people and conducting speaking engagements, she is most proud of her roles as mother, sister, aunt and confidant.

S: *Dr. Flowers is a 45-year-old African-American female physician. Once vivacious, she now feels mechanical in going through the motions of practicing medicine. She finds herself repeating a mantra: "Surely there is more to being a doctor than to be on a never-ending hamster wheel chasing abnormal labs, correcting bad choices made by patients, and having the life sucked out of me to meet unrealistic measures from insurance companies."*

O: *A fatigued, depressed physician who is grumpy and has lost interest in being at work. Her introvert traits are overpowering her other characteristics and she just wants to run away from all things medicine. She finds herself constantly playing the song "Scream" by Michael Jackson and emphasizing his words, "Just leave me alone!" Definitely thinking about quitting medicine, but to do what???*

A: *Physician burn out*
           Bored with work life
           Lack of family time
           Decreased quality of life
           Overworked, undervalued, and underpaid with a lot of debt

P: *Her dilemma- How can she find more to do with her MD degree since she traded her young adulthood to obtain it? She must reclaim her time and live the interesting and fulfilling life she chooses to live on her own terms.*

Dr. Flowers' Story

Then – Dr. Flowers was the third child and only girl of a young, single woman who was very strict and valued getting an education above all else. Her mom stressed the point: if you are going to do something, then do it right. In childhood, Dr. Flowers often enjoyed being alone and day dreaming. Becoming a physician was her dream since she was 4 years old. Not knowing how much time each career would require, she dreamed of being a doctor **and** something else, like a hairdresser, a teacher, a pianist or a chef. She believed she could do it all and would dismiss anyone who said she couldn't. Her mother didn't quite believe in her dreams. However, her father did, so he encouraged her to explore all her interests and exposed her to zoo animals, museums, and other activities. Unfortunately, she never saw a black physician until she saw the father of a popular family sitcom on television in the 1980's. During times of despair due to being poor, she dreamed of a she-ro that would help her...

The villain of my story was my own desire to leave medicine. I no longer enjoyed doing traditional family medicine because most of the patients were not motivated to get well. Unfortunately, our society has adopted some bad habits like overeating easily accessible processed foods, not being physically active and smoking. This society also has a lack of accountability for the choices made that have accumulated into chronic debilitating illnesses. Also, most patients have an unrealistic expectation of a quick fix for these long-standing health issues. In addition to this dreary outlook, our medical system is geared to pacify insurance companies and not geared to truly improve one's overall health. All of this comes together to use up the gifts and talents of those on the front line of medicine, usually the primary care physician, with no just reward.

Although I truly love helping people and have an immense love for them, I realized that I was giving too much of myself away to my patients and did not have anything left for myself or, more importantly to me, for my son. Thank God for the few sprinkles of patients that were actually eager to improve their health. I loved having an opportunity to celebrate with them when they did something wonderful. These few gave me hope, but it just wasn't enough to sustain me or to keep me on this Ferris wheel going nowhere. I love the patients and always work hard for them, but I didn't love the constraints that I worked under. That job left me wondering, "What about me and my happiness? Am I not important too?"

I knew it was time for a serious career change when I started becoming physically ill whenever I arrived at the clinic for work. My symptoms included tension headaches, loss of appetite (for a foodie like me, that is serious), depressed disposition at work, decreased interest in relating to the clinic staff and decrease in desire and energy to spend quality time with family and friends. I had little energy to play and be jovial with my son. Unlike my normal relaxed, approachable, comedic self, I just wanted to be left alone and day dreamed of being on a beach without anyone there to want or need anything from me.

In evaluating myself, I used an approach of self-examination of looking at myself in the mirror and asking, "What is wrong? How are you going to fix this? You solve other people problems every day. Physician, heal thyself." The problem: I was burned out from traditional family medicine and the redundancy of the type of problems seen in a primary care clinic. I was bored! There are only so many ways to discuss diabetes, hypertension, high cholesterol and obesity. The lackluster effort of some of the patients themselves also discouraged me. One day, I told a very non-compliant patient, "This is your body we're discussing. I don't have diabetes and high blood pressure, but you do. So, tell me what you want to do. Do you want to come see me socially periodically or are you going to participate in your care and make this a team effort? I can't care more about your health than you do. Actually, I just won't."

Amazingly, she was receptive to my honesty and she began to comply with treatment. She was one out of many to do so.

I was also lonely-- missing out on quality family time due to work-related issues like working long hours, having many strenuous days or the intrusion of taking call at night or on weekends. I realized I was programmed from childhood to do my best in every situation; thus, my insistence to do be a "good doctor." I felt like I was my own worst enemy by pushing myself to work harder in such a malignant configuration as our medical care system. Eventually, all these malignant factors took their toll and affected my quality of life. I was left with the aftermath of feeling overworked, undervalued and underpaid for my efforts and nothing to give my loved ones.

The realization that I was running on empty and losing the joy I once had in practicing medicine stimulated my drive to find different ways to use my M.D. degree that may offer me more personal satisfaction or personal fulfillment. The steps I took were simple but required me to let go of my traditional idea of what a doctor's day should look like.

The first step: I signed up with several recruiting firms. This step was so simple but proved to be and still is one of the most valuable. I literally started getting five to fifteen job offers daily. It was crazy at first, but later I felt wanted, meaning I realized my options. If I didn't want to stay at this job, I had many more jobs to consider with different and sometimes better benefits. This step alone gave me the confidence to consider what else might be beyond what I already knew.

The second step: I left my full-time job. Now this wasn't as scary as it may seem simply because I had a good amount of money saved. Taking the advice of many financial experts, I had more than enough to cover all my bills, sports fees and other activities for my son for several months. I also felt comfortable because I was no longer married, thus I didn't have to worry about anyone else having a say over how my money was being spent (i.e. a husband who had bad financial habits). This financial comfort zone made me feel relaxed and not pressured to rush into another job, but rather truly explore. Like never before, I was grateful that I had lived below my means and was a good money saver versus a high spender who lived a life to impress others "because I am a doctor."

The third step, now that I had ample time on my hands, was to reset the tone of my house. I focused my energy on being the type of mother I felt my son deserved and moved away from being the distracted, always in rush, always tired from work, slightly grumpy mother he knew. After my divorce, I finally saw my son thrive in school and at home. He became eager to do household chores since he felt like he was helping me be happier. His confidence grew too. I finally had more energy and found creative ways to give him positive reinforcement. I, too, felt like a different woman, one that I actually liked.

The fourth step: I developed a work-from-home schedule. Being very goal-oriented, I needed some kind of structure to my day after getting my son to school and before picking him up again. Initially, I researched non-clinical jobs for doctors. I had meetings 1-2 times a week with other healthcare contacts I developed over the years. These meetings helped me tune into niches that weren't being filled at the time. I took my time to evaluate those openings. Several of these meetings led to jobs I accepted, such as being a medical consultant, supervising an independent nurse practitioner, doing house calls, becoming a medical director for a hospice company, and several of the public speaking engagements that I've done. Many times, I truly had to work on letting go of the idea that I alone must save everyone around me. Just because someone wanted me to do a job, didn't mean I had to feel compelled to comply. It had to be a good fit for me and what I wanted my life to be like.

The fifth step: I learned the power of saying "no." I finally took time to ask if a job would help me fulfill my personal goals. If my answer was that it would not, or that it would require me to compromise time with my son, then I was comfortable declining that job offer. I called these jobs "time fillers" that weren't worth me leaving my home or my son and may block other great opportunities. Most of these jobs had ridiculously low wages, required long hours away from my son, were farther away than I cared to drive in traffic, or mileage wasn't reimbursed thus costing me money to go do that job. Before I knew it, I had pieced together a career of interesting jobs that I worked simultaneously, and I controlled my time completely, making me an independent contractor.

The sixth step: I practiced getting comfortable in my skin as an independent contractor. Because I didn't have one stationary work place, I essentially perfected hiding in plain sight. I escaped the "clawing sessions" from pharmaceutical and equipment reps for me to use their products. I truly enjoyed being untouchable. No one could figure me out because they couldn't understand what I did for work, when I worked, or where I worked. For me, outside approval was not important anymore. I knew what I did, when I did it, and where I did everything, and I was content with that. However, my greatest joy came from having inner peace when I found balance between my personal and professional worlds, was the mother I wanted to be and felt fulfilled with doing cool and interesting jobs.

The final step: I joined groups of other like-minded physicians such as Artemis Medical Society, Mocha Medicine, Physician Moms Group, Rowe Docs, Physician Side Gigs, and Superwoman Survival Group, just to name a few. In these groups I met women like me. Intelligent. Beautiful. Compassionate. Inspirational. Conscious. Adventurous. Unpredictable. They held me accountable to be honest with myself and others, uplifted my spirits to feel okay about whatever I was going through and supported me unconditionally so that I knew I was not alone in my struggle to live my best life. These women were superheroes in their own realms. We laughed, cried, and stood together. We combined our super powers for the betterment of ourselves, our families, our communities and our world. The most wonderful part is I still have them in my life.

Now -- Dr. Flowers is the she-ro that she wished she had when she was growing up. Her super-power is making others feel loved, significant or that they matter. By day, she is a family medicine physician who is proficient in urgent care, occupational care, hospice and palliative care, and recently added being a sub-specialist in neuropathy to her resume'. She is also a community activist, public speaker, mentor, author and the founder of a teen girl talk series called B.R.A.I.Ns & Beauty. Besides her professional duties, she is most proud to be a mother to one, an aunt to a few, a sister and a confidant to many. Juggling many jobs at once and excelling in each of them has become her trademark.

Charmaine Gregory, MD

"If you're thinking about quitting medicine, ask yourself this question: 'What is the real reason why you want to walk away? Could it be that you need to reclaim your joy so that you can practice on your own terms?"

Charmaine Gregory, MD

She has served countless patients, taught resident doctors and medical students for 13 years as Clinical Faculty at St. Joseph Mercy Ann Arbor in Michigan, following Emergency Medicine Residency training at Duke

University Medical Center. She has been honored as a nominee for the Golden Apple teaching award by the resident doctors she teaches several years in a row. She is an active member of the Clinical Practice Committee for the Emergency Medicine Physician Group, PC. She serves as a Peer Coach providing feedback on communication techniques for Emergency providers and facilitates talks with healthcare providers about burnout, wellness, and work-life balance. Most recently, Dr. Gregory co-authored *The Chronicles of Women in White Coats* and was featured in several Doximity articles as well as a Medscape portfolio on women in medicine.

Outside of medicine, her passion to pursue wellness and work-life balance led to the establishment of the virtual greatness and wellness coaching company Fervently Fit with Charmaine, LLC. Wellness, fitness coaching and holistic nutritional supplementation serve as extensions of clinical service by focusing on preventative methods for health and wellness maintenance. She is a speaker and physician coach addressing topics related to physician wellness, physician burnout, and work-life balance. In addition, she is certified to teach live group fitness classes in MMA (Mixed Martial Arts) and offers group fitness instruction to colleagues at national meetings.

Contact information:

Email: charmaine@ferventlyfitwithcharmaine.com

Phone: 240-FIT-DOC8

S: 37-year-old AA female presents with fading love for her clinical practice. She notes feeling physically pained going into work and serving patients. She finds it difficult to spring out of bed in time for her night shifts. Her joy for serving patients had evaporated.

O: Procrastination, neglect of family, desire to not get out of bed, loss of impetus, a depressed mood, loss of joy.

A: DDx 1. Clinical depression

    2. Burnout

    3. Depressed mood

    4. Disinterest

    5. Apathy

P: Rerouting the focus from negative feelings to an outward focus. Taking time out for self-care, including personal development, content consumption and working out regularly. Helping others recognize and overcome the symptoms of burnout. Realizing that when I feel the tug of the negative energy from the abyss, immediate endorphin surges, mindful pauses, and helping others thwarts the rapid descent expeditiously.

Dr. Gregory's Story

It was a warm sunny day in Buffalo, NY. The sun was making its coveted three-month appearance and felt like new life as the beams of light stroked my face ever so gently. Today was a special day--a day that was cloaked with a lengthy backstory and riddled with pride and elation. My family had traveled from far away to share this moment and the pride burst through every single pore of their beings. As my uncle Richard captured the moments, as he is adept at doing behind his camera lens, I had to pinch myself to confirm that I was not in a dream state. As I walked across the stage and shook hands with faculty, I was close to tears. A myriad of emotions coursed through me; happiness, relief, sadness, fear and doubt.

A dream realized. A mother stands proudly as the evidence and reward of her sacrifice walks across the stage, flanked by a dais rich with seasoned mentors and educators. A daughter is overcome by emotion as the culmination of years of work embodied in a replica of the prize for diligence is thrust into her hands. She is joyful, sad, scared and excited all at once. She spoke it many years before when she ran into her mom's room and boldly declared that she would be a doctor when she grew up. She had no idea the tortuosity of the path to her goal. She was not contaminated by the failures, pressures and obstacles that could thwart the realization of her dream. She dreamt boldly, with the only thought that she could do anything she set her mind to. From humble beginnings, raised by a single mom who sold everything and emigrated to the United States with two suitcases and $40, leaving behind everything she knew to provide the opportunity for her 10-year-old daughter who had a dream of greatness, to this moment when the audacious declaration of an eight-year-old child becomes a reality.

The first time I was referred to as Dr. Gregory, I had to pinch myself. On one hand, I was proud to have stuck to the path and reached the goal. On the other hand, I felt an overwhelming sense of doubt. "What if I mess up? What if I harm a patient? What if I write the wrong dose? How can they trust me? I have no experience." Thank God for senior residents and attendings! There were several moments in my life when I experienced the Imposter Syndrome, that moment when self-doubt supersedes the fact that you have the chops to do the job, find the solution or figure out the problem and fear overcomes you. That is the epitome of the Imposter Syndrome.

There I was—top of the class in high school while managing to finish at age 16. Fast forward to college, where the bar was raised exponentially and a 4.0 was a prize I was only afforded one of the eight semesters I was there. This top student was seeking out help from TAs and professors constantly to stay afloat and maintain a grade point average above 3.2 at a school that was heavily focused on science and engineering. There was a point when the student who was on the apex of the food chain transitioned forcibly to a lesser rung, and the well-earned and struggled-for C becomes the ultimate prize. Despite the shock and morale-busting rigors of college, I refused the status of the interloper and instead focused on victory despite adversity. My "WHY" at that time was the dream of my preteen years that I had to realize and the vision of my mother who made the ultimate sacrifice for my future. Even in my youth, I figured out my weaknesses quickly and worked on making them strengths. When that path was not feasible, I sought to find an alternate one. So, it turns out that I am not one of those people who can go into a standardized test and blow it out of the water without marked diligence and preparation. I trained for the SAT and improved my score from the PSAT by almost 300 points. My vision and presumed destiny were to become a physician. Medical schools required a standardized test - the MCAT. With this perceived weakness acknowledged and finding a hurdle to overcome to get to the goal, I sought an alternate pathway. My solution was to circumvent the MCAT and get accepted into Medical school based on my college grades and SAT scores.

They say that you cannot run from your weaknesses and your demons. Separation led me to a unique solution to medical school admission during my sophomore year and I was granted a seat upon graduation from college if I maintained at least a 3.2 GPA for the remaining two and a half years. Medical school was challenging in the volume of material to internalize and the familiarization of a new language. Despite this, I managed to do fairly well during the first two years. Then, that demon arose. USMLE Step 1. I went into the forest to claim my Excalibur and instead I was met by my weaker, less confident and cowering self who stood in the way of the prize and handed me instead a failing grade on Step 1. These were dark times for me. I wept not only because I was faced with the possibility of not being able to continue to the clinical years but also because I was disappointed in the girl who was top of her class all through the primary and secondary years. Had my mother made the wrong decision, displacing us from our homeland, leaving everything behind to start from scratch in a foreign land to support her child's declaration that she would be a doctor? Yes, I fell down. It was not the first time and would definitely not be the last. The key is that I did not stay down. I got up, dusted off my shoulders, wiped away my tears and looked for a solution. With no real guidance or idea where to start, I just did as many questions as I could get my hands on. Thankfully, I passed on the retake. However, this demon followed me all the way to my fourth year when I was getting set to apply to residency. Problem: Emergency medicine was very competitive back then, even more so today, and that demon hung over my head like an anvil. Solution: Applying to 44 programs. I matched at the exact place that I needed to be, Duke University. Training at Duke provided a foundation that is unparalleled and has led to the launch of a long career in emergency medicine.

When I left residency and started my position as an attending, the dream that started so long ago was finally materializing. I was so excited, ready to take on the world, ready to save lives and serve patients as I was trained to do. I was surprised to find that my path towards fulfilling my destiny was not as straightforward as I had been led to believe. As a result, I found myself playing several roles as I struggled to find my niche. I did fellowships in education and education research, I served as the Medical Student Site Director, I attended conferences and became certified in palliative care in the Emergency Department along the way. I loved my job, I loved the ED, but I just floundered trying to find my niche in my field. Why was this necessary? It was necessary because that is what I had been told, read someplace or two and had since internalized.

One day, it was like a blink and then my eyes opened to a situation that was surreal when it happened. How did I make the transition from excited, engaged, young attending to this broken shell who "white-knuckles" the steering wheel on work nights? Where did the fire go? There I sat in the parking lot, engine still running, frozen hands in the clenched position gripping the steering wheel. The clock on the dashboard shouted in bright red digits, "10:55 pm!!!!" My heart began to pound with a cadence commensurate with scared prey as a predator approached. My mental soundtrack kicked in a repetitive message in monotone, "Come on Charmaine. Let go of the steering wheel. Get out of the car. Go to work. You have a job to do." Night after night, when the alarm clock blared as a signal that my sweet dream-laden anchor nap was over, I struggled to raise myself up to the sitting position, swing my legs onto the floor and then engage my hip flexors to propel my body into the standing position. The deeper I sank into the abyss, the more I struggled to get myself to go to work each night. How did I get to this place? This place devoid of light, joy, and motivation had crept up on me like a clandestine marauder.

This stealthy onslaught stole my joy for medicine and its practice. It robbed me of the brilliance of a dream realized after so many years of sacrifice and resilience. I felt so weak! Is this not the person who left her homeland at age

10, arriving alone a month before her mother to start a new life in a new country to become a physician? I am the strong person that would take two NYC buses to school each day at age 10 completely on my own. During high school, I sought out opportunities for academic enrichment and traveled two hours by train to get to independent league basketball practice every Saturday in order to improve the game learned later than my peers. When doors closed for me, I would look for solutions and workarounds, refusing to give up. This is the same woman who made sure every summer was spent doing some form of academic enrichment through high school and college despite having to travel far away from home. After all, I left home at age 16 to attend college, so being away from home was not a novelty. Years of failing, getting back up, stepping out on faith and being rewarded with growth and progression towards my ultimate goal could not succor this broken me.

As life would have it, burnout caught me unprepared and unaware. It was not just the stresses of making high-stakes decisions with little or no data, which is par for the course in emergency medicine. It was not the constraints on my work induced by the administration who does not come in contact with actual patients in the clinical environment. It was not the cumbersome weight of the electronic medical record (EMR) and its idiosyncrasies. It was not the furtive knee injury, which derailed my fitness and wellness during the year that it remained undiagnosed, that ravaged my right quadriceps and decreased the range of motion of my right knee. It was not the growth of my girth and the ill-fitting clothing that provoked the purchase of two sizes above the size I wore for years. It was not the bearing of three cherubs in the span of four years. It was not the fact that I was eight years out of residency and reaching the point in my career where burnout is the highest risk. It was not any one of these reasons. It was likely a bit of all of these in culmination that trapped me in the vice grip of despair that is burnout.

It is ironic that I was rescued from the abyss of burnout by resources outside of medicine. Our cherubs are homeschooled and as a result, I had become involved in various homeschool moms' groups. One of the moms I befriended reached out to me one day and invited me to join a fitness accountability group she was hosting. That simple action led to a beautiful cascade of events that led to my recovery. I fell in love with fitness again. Remember I mentioned that I was an athlete in high school? I played lacrosse, field hockey and ran track in college. Along with the return to my previous clothing size came a gargantuan mental transformation. Not only was I working out six times a week, but also working on myself by reading personal development books. There was a joy, confidence, and fervor that rose up, which was quiescent during my time of struggle. It was real to me when I started a business focusing on helping other busy women reclaim their fitness mojos. Then the miracle happened. I found that I loved helping others find their light and regain confidence. My shoulders were pushed back a bit more, my chin began to raise, my eyes looked forward, and my heart was renewed by helping others. When I was confronted by a former patient who had been seen during my nadir, I was shocked to get feedback about how sad I appeared and how grumpy I came across. Anyone who knows me knows that I am a happy person at baseline. Smiles are given freely with the occasional belly laugh. The person that was in the belly of the beast of burnout was not me. It was a shell of me. An empty shell. My true self was awakened by paying attention to my physical and psychological self and the glorious side effect was I found joy in medicine again.

No longer would I have to will, sometimes even bribe myself to get my rear out of the bed when that alarm sounded. No longer was I gripping the steering wheel, sitting in the parking lot, until the blood seemed to escape from my fingers. No longer did I dread going in to serve the patients I trained so long to be prepared to help.

For me, paying attention to self-care, sharing my journey with others, helping others reclaim their fitness mojo and developing positive energy within me was my path out of the chasm of burnout. I found joy in learning about business management, marketing, social media, nutrition and fitness. This was a smooth transition into engaging in leadership training in emergency medicine because of the confidence and positive outlook that running this type of business afforded. There were fears that I learned to face. Like so many millions of people, I have a deep fear of public speaking. This experience has taught me to look that fear in the eyeballs and do it anyway. Through social media, I faced my fear daily by documenting my fitness journey and sharing what I was learning both in my personal development and about fitness. This led to opportunities to face my fear and make an impact on my colleagues. Because of my journey and my joyful rebirth, I was able to teach group fitness classes at the American College of Emergency Physicians (ACEP) at the national meeting in the fall of 2017. Currently, I am working on several wellness projects that will impact my colleagues in emergency medicine.

Fighting for my self-care led to a renewed joy for my craft and a desire to serve patients every night that I have the privilege to work. Creating a business that focused on others led to collaborations, networking and development on a personal brand with the goal to inspire, empower and invigorate. I did burnout. I did not recognize it at the time. I accidentally found a bright path out of the burnout crevasse. Now, not only do I want to practice medicine, but I also want to help others who are going through this pain so that it can be clear that burnout is not a terminal destination. I survived burnout and now I thrive. My mission is to make sure that the path for you is clear so that you can circumvent the burnout fissure and practice medicine on your terms. My personal brand reaches into the areas of fitness coaching, wellness coaching, inspirational speaking and nutrition. Be strong. Be brave. Unleash your greatness!

Zarinah Hud, DO

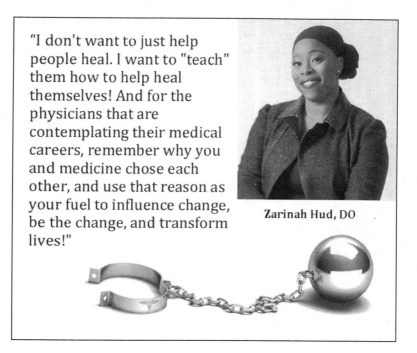

"I don't want to just help people heal. I want to "teach" them how to help heal themselves! And for the physicians that are contemplating their medical careers, remember why you and medicine chose each other, and use that reason as your fuel to influence change, be the change, and transform lives!"

Zarinah Hud, DO

Dr. Zarinah (Dr. Zee) Hud is a Physiatrist (Physical Medicine and Rehabilitation specialist and fellowship-trained Integrative Sports and Pain Medicine). She is a wife, mother, author, speaker, businesswoman, and

CEO/Founder of her medical practice Rebound Sports & Rehab, LLC in Atlanta, GA. She received her undergraduate degree in Pre-med Biology Summa Cum Laude and went on to pursue a career in medicine while attending Ohio University College of Osteopathic Medicine, graduating in top 10% of her class. She then went on to attend residency at Thomas Jefferson as the 1st African American woman in her program in more than 30 years of its existence. From there, she wanted to expand her knowledge and training further so that she could equip her medical "toolbox" as robustly as possible. So, she was accepted to a competitive Integrative Sports Medicine fellowship as one of the first women and the first African American woman ever accepted to the program in Erie, Pennsylvania. It was there that she honed her passion to help relieve pain and improve overall function of the human body using the body's innate abilities to help heal itself and incorporating minimally invasive, integrative and natural treatment programs to promote the body's healing capabilities. Some of these treatments included regenerative injection therapy (i.e. platelet-rich plasma and prolotherapy), homeopathic medications, integrative nutrition as medicine, sleep hygiene, acupuncture, manual therapy, dry-needling and more. Dr. Zarinah did all of this as a newlywed just after medical school and delivered her first child while in fellowship training. Her husband knew when he married her that life was probably going to be a bit "unconventional," with a few bumps and bruises along the way. They were both dedicated to each other, so they took the journey together and created a beautiful life filled with love that they share with their two young girls that keep their lives full and busy!

Dr. Zarinah was born the 4th child of five in the home to a father also named Dr. Hud (PhD) and a mother that was full-time mother and professional in the mental health field as a Licensed Clinical Social Worker. They instilled in her to always strive for and expect excellence from herself, never settle for mediocrity, failure is not an option and lead with your morals and work ethic. Despite her accomplishments, the road to her successes was not smooth. And in order for her to live the life she'd always envisioned, she knew some things would have to change. She was a driven person that always knew she would become a doctor and now that she had it, is she really thinking about quitting medicine? Well, she knew deep down inside that she had not reached her fullest potential or even tapped the surface, and often felt that the "health care system" was not designed to serve patients the way she longed for.

She endured a string of employment positions that left her disenchanted and worn out with not only how she was treated as a highly trained and skilled physician in the pain management industry, but also what her patients were subjected to as "healthcare." She never really felt like she was truly providing optimal "health" or "care" to her patients. So, after a few years out of fellowship, she reluctantly struck out on her own to develop her own medical practice, Rebound Sports & Rehab, LLC to finally practice medicine on her own terms. This meant she could develop treatment programs and implement lifestyle programs that would truly have long-term impact on her patients' lives, not just decreasing and/or masking symptoms. Instead, she now had the opportunity to teach her patients *how* to rebound their health and obtain Pain Freedom™ long-term. She now runs a concierge medical practice, hosts an online TV Show "Rebound Your Health TV w/Dr. Zee," best-selling author of *"Everybody Has 15 Minutes: 15 Minute Meals to Your Pain Freedom,"* offers a one-on-one MVP Pain Freedom Coaching Program, courses, webinars, speaks and writes for the media and provides rehabilitation consultant services for nearby hospitals. She is still expanding products and services to her Dr. Zarinah, LLC, which will continue to provide her with more ways to serve and more "Time Freedom" for her and her family.

S: 37-year-old female Sports and Integrative pain doctor, with a husband and 2 toddlers. She does Locum Tenens a couple hours away from home and serves as a medical consultant for a nearby hospital, working more than 60 hours per week and bringing work home. She presents with "discontentment and exhaustion." She's unfulfilled and disappointed while working professionally, leaving her feeling overwhelmed at work and at home. Constantly running into employment that were borderline "pill mills" and a job that refused to pay her for services she rendered that equaled to thousands of dollars. Being pushed by employers and insurance companies to treat pain using the "easy way out" and "the quickest way" possible. This often meant trying to evaluate, assess, provide education, review labs and radiology images, and examine the patient in 15 minutes. This was to be followed up with a prescription for one or more schedule II medications (i.e. opioids, sedatives, anxiolytics, etc.). Both patient and doctor were on hamster wheels that just seemed to never have an end point and never seemed to truly make a real difference in their healing

51

or function. To make matters worse, she feels like she is missing out on some very pivotal moments with her two young children and creating memories with her husband. She has a heightened awareness of what is lacking for herself, personally and professionally, as well as for her patients. So, she yearns for a change that will be more fulfilling to her and the people she serves so that she can wake up each day knowing that she is truly empowering and helping to transform lives long-term, and at the same time reclaim her "Time Freedom."

O: She is stable, with a joyful smile and energetic personality. Her eyes tell it all. The depths of her sincere passion and love for humanity and people she meets are immediately evident and infectious. She is ambitious and driven by "purpose" and not "paper" (i.e. money). She is dressed in royal blue scrubs and long sleeve shirt under her top, black Dansko shoes and hair pulled back into a bun under a black fashionable headscarf, along with small diamond hoop earrings. Both children are younger than five *years old. Her supportive husband works full time in the mental health field. Her favorite place to be is among family and the beach. However, both are becoming rare occurrences due to her professional schedule.*

A: *She is a wife, mother, best-selling author, public speaker, CEO and medical practice owner that wants more out of life beyond her titles. She is seeking freedom!*

P: *Treatment plan will include for her to step into her purpose without apologies. Saying "NO" to some things is actually saying "YES" to yourself and your freedom! When you are free and living your true purpose, it gives others the courage and permission to do the same in their own lives. Her treatment plan should also include continuing to optimize her medical degree beyond the clinic, while creating opportunities and fostering relationships with people and entities that share the same values for your patients and audience. This mindset shift will allow her to have more mental space and time to put energy toward the* *things she desires the most, which include creating more family memories and enjoying more beaches.*

Dr. Zarinah's Story

I was on the third job in three years after leaving the previous ones due to unethical practices and pressure from non-clinical administrators for me to prescribe more schedule II medications. They also wanted me to see more patients in my nine-hour clinic, which consistently became 14-16-hour days. Administrators continuously double-booked my schedule with chronic pain patients that each needed more than 15 minutes of my time. Then, it really hit the fan emotionally. While working this last position, I was eight months pregnant, stressed out, commuting two hours one way from home, returning home after my then one-year-old was already in bed. In the midst of all of this, the employer tells me that he doesn't have enough money to pay me and promises to pay me the next pay period. Of course, that never happened. Suddenly, I felt trapped, and the challenges didn't end there. A month later, I delivered my second child, and moments following her delivery while still lying in the hospital bed, I found myself facing one of the biggest challenges in my life. Lying in a hospital bed just a few hours after delivering my second child, I was experiencing medical complications that resulted in vascular compromise, affecting my ability to feel and/or move the left side of my body. This affected blood flow to the brain. After a few days of managing post-partum pre-eclampsia cardiovascular compromise and trying to prevent seizure and stroke, I was finally stable enough to be discharged home. Once I was finally home, I unfortunately had to return to the hospital in the middle of the night within a couple of days. I was experiencing severe pain in my lower limbs, confusion and a severe gut-wrenching headache. For the next year and a half, I underwent multiple tests, labs, brain scans and chest scans. It wasn't easy. I didn't work for a year following the birth of my second child because my symptoms fluctuated so frequently. However, two years after being diagnosed with a rare form of Subclavian Steal Syndrome, I am living well and healthy. Undoubtedly, I attribute this to my diet and healthy lifestyle choices. This has made me more determined than ever to share with the world what I've learned through personal experience along with my expertise in pain management using traditional and integrative approaches. I'm just so thankful that I'm here to serve, be a wife, mother, sister and daughter to those whom I love the most. It's truly such a gift. I would be lying if I said that, at that time in my life, I didn't experience deep worry and sadness that fluctuated throughout that first 18 months, but I had to make a choice: Will I accept mediocrity? Will I allow myself to continue to be devalued? Will I accept going through the motions in the clinic day to day? Or, will finally step into my purpose without hesitation and without apologies? I chose the latter. It was then I decided to surround myself with big thinkers, people who think outside the box, people who want more out of life than their current hamster wheel. I also knew that the woman I was during that period of my life, was not the woman that I wanted my young girls to be. I wanted to create a legacy that they could be proud of and that I would have no regrets with. I began to build my "tribe" of supporters that would guide me, pull me back when needed, push me when needed, hold me accountable and love on me through my ups and downs. I was able to revamp my medical practice model, launch new programs and services, build new businesses, speak and teach more often in media and from the stage and spend more time with my family while I was doing it. Now, I provide services and programs to my patients and clients with a greater than 90% positive improvement. I jokingly share that it's both my blessing and my curse. Getting people better to the point where they don't need me because I give them the long-term treatment, strategies and tools they need to succeed. I also get the opportunity to provide programs to people from all over the world right from the comfort of my own home. I learned to create the life I seek, which really is just bringing me full circle, because it indeed is the same message my parents taught me as a little girl. I am now more certain than ever of my value, my talents, my skills, my passions, and most importantly my purpose. This time around I make no apologies for it and graciously can say that I am the MVP (Most Valuable Person) in my life, which allows me to have even more to pour into others. I used to believe that you can't be humble and profess greatness at the same time. However, I now know that we can indeed be Humbly Great! I challenge you to do the same.

Rebekah Hughey, MD

"I intend to be remembered as helping to advance our collective ability to use the power of the mind to transform human existence. If the desire exists in your mind, so does the way to achieve it--the two are one."

Rebekah Hughey, MD

My name is Dr. Rebekah Hughey and I am a board certified, integrative family medicine doctor. I am a writer, artist, healer, mother, public speaker, consultant, entrepreneur, sports enthusiast, mental athlete, teacher, leadership coach, life coach and hypnotist.

This project is significant to me because I believe in the collective good that comes about when we as a group of like-minded physicians, inspired by stories of our peers' success, make the decision to harness all our passions and talents to recreate our lives on our terms. We can then leverage our power in society, using this reclaimed time and energy, to become agents of change. I also believe in my particular gift of teaching people how to use the power of their unconscious minds to tap into the field of infinite potential in order to transform their physical, mental, and emotional beings.

I am a native of Pittsburgh, Pennsylvania and grew up on the east side of town in the Homewood community. I finished high school at The Ellis School in Pittsburgh, then completed my bachelor's degree with a minor in mathematics at Spelman College in Atlanta, GA. I earned my medical degree from the University of North Carolina at Chapel Hill School of Medicine and completed my residency and faculty development fellowship at

Southern Regional AHEC, a Duke University community program. I concurrently attended Duke University to complete a certificate in clinical leadership. After becoming a diplomate of the American Board of Integrative and Holistic Medicine, I earned my certification in clinical hypnosis under the tutelage of mentors such as Dr. Holly Forester-Miller of Durham, NC and Betty Alice Erickson, daughter of Dr. Milton Erickson. I am a proud graduate of the William C. Friday fellowship for Human Relations and currently sit on the executive board of the Wildacres Leadership Initiative in North Carolina.

My favorite authors include Napoleon Hill, Dr. Wayne Dyer, Eckhart Tolle, Dr. Deepak Chopra, Dr. Bruce Lipton, Dr. Joe Dispenza, David Cameron Gikandi, Sadhguru, Orson Scott Card, and Terry Brooks.

At the time of this writing, I am inspired by my most recent read, *Madison Park*, by Dr. Eric Motley.

You can learn more about my work, including my blog, signature coaching program, speaking topics and uses for hypnosis at my website lifthealing.com.

S: 38-year-old integrative family medicine doctor living everyone else's dream but her own.

O: She knew she was a healer at age 8 and thought medical school was the way to go. She sacrificed other interests and hobbies throughout college and medical school in order to reach this goal. She neglected too many parts of herself in the process.

A: 38-year-old family medicine doctor yearning to reclaim her sense of self, honor her gifts and nurture her inner being at all costs.

P: Change from full-time to part-time work and use reclaimed time for family and starting a new venture teaching successful professionals how to harness the power of their minds, through self-hypnosis and other advanced mental techniques, in order to transform their lives.

Dr. Hughey's Story

As a child, I loved adventure—running, jumping, playing, *doing*. I explored dark spaces, turned over rocks to see what was hiding below, and climbed everything I could from fences to trees to walls and winding steps, just to see how high I could get. Sports were also a big part of my life. I ran track, played softball, hockey, basketball, and lacrosse. My aim was always to pusher harder, go faster and win. My parents gave me a firm foundation. My mother exercised religiously every morning and was a popular local dance and aerobics instructor. She also taught me the power of prayer. My father taught me how to focus my mind through meditation and to use its power to accomplish whatever I wanted.

My love for reading and adventure led me to a book series called "Choose Your Own Adventure." Each book contained multiple stories, existing in parallel. While reading one storyline, I as the story's hero would come to a point of palpable tension and would be required to make a decision. For instance, I would emerge from a cave and see a winding path leading into a dense forest. I would also see a well-worn path leading straight to the castle. If I chose the first, I'd turn to page 32. If I wanted the second, I'd turn to page 40. Each choice revealed a separate, unique journey, made possible only after a definitive choice was made. Things weren't always as they seemed, and sometimes the paths that looked the easiest and seemed to guarantee safety would lead to my demise. Often the paths that looked scary and uncertain led to amazing adventure and ultimate success.

I liken my life in medicine to one of these "Choose Your Own Adventure" books. It has been full of excitement, challenge, elation, depression, and most importantly, the ability to choose my professional fate.

Come with me on an adventure through this magical time in my life. It's sure to keep you involved, intrigued, interested, in-tune, and entranced...

I decided to be a doctor when I was eight years old. Who knows why children decide such big things at such small ages? I enjoyed school and was good in all my subjects. I especially loved art, writing, and math. As I got older and moved through middle and high school, I remained pretty well-rounded. I played multiple sports, entered art and writing competitions, and I still very much enjoyed school. This was a time in my life on which I often look back, remembering how much of this I was asked to sacrifice to have a "successful" medical career.

I continued on the path to medical school through college and finally, after much hard work and seemingly endless testing, chose to attend UNC Chapel Hill School of Medicine. I had married shortly after college and by this time had a beautiful one-year-old baby girl.

Entering medical school was like stepping through the looking glass into a completely new world. Perspectives shifted, priorities changed, and medical school demanded most of my time, energy, emotion and commitment. This was often achieved by sacrificing commitments to family, personal health and well-being, and other talents and hobbies. I also realized that I was becoming part of a system focused more on illness than on wellness. Because I saw myself as a healer, this was very disappointing, and I often questioned my decision to continue. In order to survive however, I learned to move forward no matter how uncomfortable I was. I also learned implicitly not to question the system.

This can be a lonely time without a guide—someone who knows the experience, is part of the process, and who provides wisdom and encouragement to help power through the journey. For me, this guide was Mani St. Victor. My husband and I saw him in Walmart wearing a "UNC MED" shirt and started a conversation. We became fast friends. At the time, Mani was two years ahead of me and gave me the lay of the land—who to trust, who to avoid and how to set myself up for success. Most importantly, he helped to reignite my passion for exploring the power of the mind. Through the application of his unique memory techniques, I was able to read large volumes of complicated material and remember the information without having to see it again. This helped me tremendously, boosting my confidence and ensuring my success. Not long before graduation I met another guide, Dr. Holly Forester-Miller, as part of an integrative medicine course. She is a pioneer in the field and has performed multiple surgeries using hypnosis as her only anesthesia. She taught me the art of hypnosis and deepened my respect for the power of the mind not only to enhance learning but to promote healing.

I graduated from medical school in 2008 and started my residency at a Duke University community program in Fayetteville, NC called Southern Regional Area Health Education Center (AHEC).

Residency was grueling at times, but overall was much more enjoyable than medical school. Though things were going well at work, my home life did not fare as well. I had been divorced and although remarried, was not in a good situation. In addition, I was caring for an infant daughter and was often working well over forty hours a week. People in the program were very supportive and encouraged me to complete a prestigious clinical leadership program at Duke University. I also worked to complete my certificate in Integrative Medicine. These accomplishments helped set the stage for my future work. Upon finishing, I was asked to join the faculty at the AHEC, which I gladly did. Things went well, and I was eventually asked to become assistant program director for the residency program. The challenge was that my older daughter--now a teenager--was in school in Durham where I had decided to relocate. Therefore, I had been commuting one hundred miles each way for work almost every day for two years!

I had reached that palpable point of tension in my adventure, and was being forced by the narrator of my story to make a decision:

"You are exhausted and your mental and physical health are suffering because you don't have time to exercise and are eating out a lot. You have a three- hour commute four days a week and are the single mom of a three-year-old and a teenager. Your career is going well. You have the perfect mix of clinical care, teaching, conference travel, and speaking engagements. You have just been offered the position of assistant program director for the residency program. You love the people with whom you work."

Do you choose to leave the only and best job in medicine you've known (winding path through dense forest)?

Or--

Stay, tough it out and continue to build your career. Not many people get this chance (well-worn path).

I chose the winding path.

Soon after I left, my mind and body began to heal. The impact of survival mode on my body and mind became obvious. My head became clearer and I was able to rest. I loved my job at the Durham VA, working 8:00-4:30 twenty minutes away from the house. I took the kids to and from school, cooked dinner instead of eating out, and did fun things on the weekends. I did miss the academic environment and mental stimulation that teaching provided, but the tradeoff was worth it for the moment. I found enjoyment in taking care of our military veterans. I also took the opportunity for recovery and used my renewed mental energy to bring back aspects of my life that had been shut out. I even participated in three sprint triathlons with my family. Once recovered, I began to look around and reassess the situation. I was out of survival mode and ready to thrive. I wanted to begin writing again, do more public speaking, and perfect my clinical hypnosis skills. I also began to miss teaching and travel and yearned to find a way to bring the good components of my old life into the new. It was at this time that I started my own business, Lift Healing. I had been striving with the VA for quite some time to get "permission" to officially practice integrative medicine and continually met resistance. Lift was a way for me to use my skills unencumbered. I began holistic weight loss coaching, taught healing properties of essential oils, and spoke on topics including holistic nutrition, mindfulness meditation, and creating life balance. I also completed my certification in clinical hypnosis.

Unbeknownst to me, another significant change was looming around the corner. My father had been diagnosed with colon cancer and heart failure and was having many health challenges at this time. I was grateful to have time to travel back and forth to my hometown of Pittsburgh, Pennsylvania but was very concerned about his long-term prognosis. In early 2016, my father had a series of admissions to the hospital and I made plans to live in Pittsburgh for the summer to maximize my time with him. Things did not go as planned and by the time I arrived in early June, it was obvious that he had days, not months, to live.

Watching my father die was one of the most difficult times in my life. I was also extremely grateful that I had made the lifestyle changes necessary to be able to be present with him mentally and physically during those last days. It really reminded me of how important it is to listen to my heart. I hadn't known what was coming but was prepared for it nonetheless.

It was during this summer that I made another difficult choice. Being away from North Carolina helped me to step back and think about what kind of life I wanted to return to in the fall.

Again, I was faced with a choice between two parallel universes:

Return to the VA full-time, and continue Lift as a small, part-time hobby. Have good, steady pay and remain comfortable (stop to rest beneath a shady tree)?

Or--

Go back to work part-time, expand your business, and continue to use as many of your gifts as you can (enter scary cave)?

I entered the cave. Having the opportunity to intentionally craft the details of my work life was a gift. I came back to work at twenty hours a week, which allowed me to continue caring for our military veterans, which was a priority for me. I rented an office space and began focusing on my hypnosis practice. I had the amazing opportunity to learn advanced Ericksonian hypnosis from Betty Alice Erickson, daughter of Milton Erickson, MD and to work alongside my mentor Dr. Forester-Miller. I also started a blog which teaches people how to use the power of their minds to create change. I returned to the AHEC to teach one day a week and supplemented my income working as a contract hospitalist. This way I could choose when and how often I wanted to work. I used my two free weekdays to build the business.

The transformation in my life since then has been amazing. I have a successful blog, "Awakenings," and a unique coaching program catering to successful professionals who wish to build and grow professionally while remaining centered and in integrity with their authentic selves. My program incorporates hypnotic techniques and language and teaches people how to use trance to maximize performance and productivity and enhance personal and professional relationships.

In short, over the last five years I've been able to make the change from a high stress one-dimensional life to a more balanced home and professional life, using my talents and training to create a life that honors who I was created to be. I have a loving and supportive family, including a daughter who will be joining Spelman College's class of 2022 this fall... and the adventure continues...

Elizabeth R. Oates, DDS

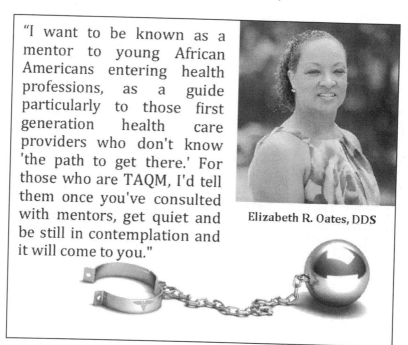

"I want to be known as a mentor to young African Americans entering health professions, as a guide particularly to those first generation health care providers who don't know 'the path to get there.' For those who are TAQM, I'd tell them once you've consulted with mentors, get quiet and be still in contemplation and it will come to you."

Elizabeth R. Oates, DDS

Dr. Oates is a native of Aberdeen, Maryland. She is a proud graduate and enthusiastic supporter of her alma mater, Hampton University. Upon graduation, she completed her doctoral studies at the first and oldest dental school in the country, The University of Maryland Dental School. She then spent two years on the Navajo Reservation, where she completed her residency training. She has experience in private practice, government contracting and institutional dental settings. In 2011, she took up the call that only 1% of Americans has ever taken and joined the US Army. She deployed to Afghanistan in 2012 in support of Operation Enduring Freedom. She continues to serve as a Lieutenant Colonel and General Dentist in the Army.

She is passionate about helping students interested in dentistry and health care studies. She has served as a personal mentor for many years to students in the Hampton University Leadership Institute and Honors College. She also volunteers her time to speak at schools, churches and health-centered events. She is a 2017 graduate of the University of Notre Dame Mendoza School of Business, Transformational Nonprofit Leadership certificate program. She is in the process of creating her own nonprofit that will develop and sustain her legacy of service for minorities with health care disparities and minority mentorship in health care.

S: 37-y.o. single female, first generation dentist, running her own five-chair start up practice. She's broke as hell, has spent her retirement, exhausted both her credit cards, her mother's credit card, borrowed money in $1500 increments from multiple friends/family. Now, she's angry as hell because she thought a Doctorate degree was supposed to guarantee her success, wealth and happiness. She feels trapped by her specialized degree. Right now, she couldn't even become an alcoholic if she wanted to because she only has enough gas to get to/from work and can't afford a single bottle of wine.

O: 37-y.o. African American female, stable, with signs of depression, sadness, regret, lack of direction and mounting desperation. No second income to supplement her during the beginnings of a start-up.

A: First-generation African American doctor in emotional, downward spiral, feeling trapped in her profession with no viable exit strategy. It is possible that she chose the wrong profession.

P: Is seeking options to leave private practice -jobs offering loan repayment relief, considering the option to join the military before she gets too old, or maybe being a long-term temporary hire so that she is not involved in the profession full-time and can explore other income-making opportunities that are less stressful.

Dr. Oates' Story

In January 2007 I was an arrogant, "I'm on top of the world" first generation AA Dentist. You couldn't tell me anything. I'd completed college and dental school on time, was handed my residency that I completed on the Navajo Reservation (I didn't have to apply) and now I was running circles around docs in the military clinic where I was providing contract services. I was proficient and confident, although I remained a conservative provider. I regularly received my quarterly bonus from the contract company I worked for because making production goals was no problem for my 33-year young self. I felt I was so good that it was a waste of my ability to produce for another company--I could produce and reap the benefits of working for myself. After all, that's what we had learned in dental school. Not to mention, all the successful dentists I'd seen were working for themselves. So, I had planned my Star Jones-like exit for February 2007. My Dad really picked a bad month to die!

I was beyond giddy to start UMD dental; I'd wanted to be a student there since seventh grade. My four years at Hampton were absolutely life-changing in the best way possible, so aside from intensified studying, this would be the same positive experience, right?? Hell No! Two weeks prior to the start of classes, the nine other black first-year students and I were introduced to the black upper-classmen and maybe a black professor or two. They were supposed to be exciting, engaging and excited for us, right? Wrong again! All I remember is being told that I better not cry in public, I better pay my Student National Dental Association dues and to avoid a few other things that would get me blackballed. They were like "F" the warm and fuzzy, welcome to PWI (primarily white institution) land, CHICK!

"Welcome to PWI land" was exactly right, and I did not adjust well. My historical black college experience at Hampton University had been the most positive and nurturing experience, so transitioning to an institution where I was a minority was a complete shock to my spirit. From day one, everyone was in intense competition with me. There was zero trust amongst my classmates, which was extremely palpable in our everyday environment. What the hell had I just gotten myself accepted into? Just like that, I was no longer excited, but nervous as hell and on edge almost every day. And then it happened... I was told a story of how a black student failed a whole year for failing one test, as if they were out to get her because she was black. That did it. My good attitude was permanently gone, and I said "hello" to paranoia, fear and resentment. Two things can be said about those four years: they were not the best four years of my life spent in one place and I could've gotten more out of the learning experience had I not had such a bad attitude.

Fast forward to the two years I spent on the Navajo Reservation, where I completed a residency and life became enjoyable again. My co-resident and I were literally the only blacks at the hospital and we had a ball! We learned a lot and had awesome life experiences, but all good things must come to an end. After residency, I spent two years at a public health department, then private practice and finally became a contractor for the Army (in 2003) back in my hometown. The contracting job was a breeze. I killed in production points, so I always received my quarterly bonus! My arrogance as a very young doctor led me to open my own practice, where I was welcomed to the ugly side of dentistry and business in a downturned economy.

I started my practice the month after my father died. I didn't even realize until a year and a half later that I was not of clear mind and sound judgement because I was consumed with a huge life change, both economically and work wise, along with grief. I'd thrown my mental state into complete shock and it was chaotic. Between my personal loss and my economic loss, I'd made it to rock bottom. I hated going to my office every day, I hated dealing with vendors and I was tired every day. I was overweight because I put on twenty pounds immediately after my dad died, and I was blowing through the business loan like it was water. I blew up my credit cards, spent almost all my retirement and did not have healthcare insurance because I couldn't afford it. In fact, there was a lot I couldn't afford to do. I couldn't take days off, I couldn't take a vacation and I had to work a second job to pay my personal bills. I could only go to work and back because I budgeted my gas where that was all I could afford to do. In my depression, I couldn't even afford to become an alcoholic because a bottle of wine was not in the budget. Life became questionable: "Was this why I went to dental school? Why didn't somebody tell me that this life style sucked? So, this is the life of a doctor? This is some bullshit. Who thought this was glamorous? I am a good person, I don't deserve for my life to end up like this..." These became my daily and nightly thoughts! I wanted to quit dentistry altogether, but I felt so trapped between business debt, student loan debt and social pressures that come with being a doctor and possessing a highly specialized degree. Oh, God, where was my out?! I had talked everyone to death with all my personal issues, so it was time to go Kanye West, "...I've been talking to God for so long, and if you look at my life he's finally talking back..."

I sold the practice December 2010 and at age 37, went to Army basic training for officers in January 2011. Bootcamp was the time in my life that I chose to consciously revamp my attitude and my mental toughness. I couldn't run worth a damn and I knew passing the PT test was going to be subject to me not being scared or giving up. I completed bootcamp successfully all while testing out my new and improved attitude toward challenges! Then, there was deployment to Afghanistan. I remember when my commander brought me in a room by myself to tell me that I was at the top of the deployment list... if you could've seen his face! He was so nervous and worried that he'd tried to get me out of it unbeknownst to me. After he gave his "you're likely to deploy" speech, he held his breath. I looked at him as calmly as I could and said "Sir, I will go, it will be ok". The fact that it seemed ok dropped the weight from his shoulders and he stayed in touch with me during deployment until he knew it was truly ok. That, and many other experiences since I've been in the Army, have taught me that if I projected worry, then I worried those around me. However, when I projected calmness, confidence and positivity, it seemed to work out better for me. And I've never. Looked. Back. My student loans were paid off within three years. I no longer worry about income, and I have time to pursue my purpose in life. I'd finally found something that worked for me and doing so allowed me to find my niche.

I started mentoring in 2015, when a classmate of mine from Hampton asked me if I would mentor the young ladies in his leadership program that told him they were interested in dentistry. I agreed but didn't really know what I'd say. Would I complain and tell them what a rough life this is? Would I tell them not to enter this field at all? I would tell them neither. As a matter of fact, mentoring his girls helped me find my purpose. The light went on! What I started realizing was that these young girls would be first-generation doctors, that they knew absolutely nothing about the journey or how to get there, and whenever we engaged, they were so thankful for any and all that I shared. There you have it. I was able to give freely what I felt like I never really got. Now I will admit all things work together for the greater good. I learned that having stability in a job, having excellent benefits, having my student loans paid off, having better than average time off and being pretty healthy are the life requirements that my personality needed to thrive. I am a happy camper in life, and because I am secure in my "seat," I am helping others to a seat at the same table. I often tell my mentees that finding your niche and what you need for your life out of your career is highly based on personality. I've met most of the career criteria for my personality, so I am pleased. I'd never say satisfied because complacency is the work of the devil. To date, my mentees include: an orthopedic surgery resident, dental students and undergrads. I follow the same formula with all my girls and they all have my cell phone number. They know that they can call and text me anytime, and that we can discus life, school and career. "Let's talk about it, get past it and get you through it to your success." That's mentoring. This for me is purpose. I used to tell people, "I know what my purpose is, and I know what it will look and feel like, I just don't know the path I have to take to get there." Mentoring my girls has been such a source of satisfaction for me that I have decided to start a non-profit dedicated to mentoring and educating people to be literate about their health care-specifically first generation African American young ladies. I've learned if they can't see you and reach out and touch you, then in their world, you do not exist.

Well I am here.

I learned the importance of community service from my mother and from Hampton University, so joining a sorority based on public service, volunteering for various community service programs, speaking at churches and schools all felt like the right things to do. Starting my own nonprofit was the natural progression from these things because God privileged me with this higher level of education that most people will never have the opportunity to get. So, my job is to help those that want it, to get there and to help translate "health" into plain English for my people. This is why I am here.

Without reservation, I can say that I am a healthy, sane, thriving dentist. Equal doses of work, adventures with friends and family, mentoring my girls and public service make me whole. I enjoy my life fully now. The only regret I have in these 18 years was my poor attitude so many years ago. Shout out to how much time and energy I wasted on the negative. Positive is here to stay. The best is yet to come.

Cwanza Pinckney, MD

"Statistics show that people who engage in creative arts and passions are exceedingly happier than people who abide by living in the mundane existence of the "I don't have [time] for that" mentality. If you are not exercising your creative passions you are not using a whole side of your brain."

Cwanza Pinckney, MD

Dr Cwanza is a nationally recognized board-certified emergency physician, self-taught mix DJ, author, speaker and life performance coach. Dr Cwanza developed a deep love for medicine through mentorship and love for patient care, but quickly learned medicine in the real world came with unexpected challenges. After eight years in clinical medicine, Dr Cwanza recognized a deep disconnect from her love for medicine and lack of independence as a physician. She became discouraged by career and personal life choices and realized she was not living her best life. Despite the ups and downs, Dr Cwanza rekindled her love for music and started an additional career as a DJ. Dr Cwanza's creative mind flourished and through the journey of acceptance of self-revelation, purpose, mindset mastery and personal development, she found a new joy in medicine and music. This has blossomed into a thriving emergency medicine career, a national and international mobile and corporate DJ business, a mobile medical concierge business and podcasting.

S: 40-year-old African American female, Emergency Medicine Attending, proud LGBTQ community member, and self-proclaimed "Happy Unicorn." She is currently suffering from a case of "WTF" syndrome relating to her discontent as an attending physician in community practice. She is the medical director and assistant medical director for a large "democratic" emergency physician group. She is plagued by frustrations related to the increasing demands of charting until her carpal tunnel is flared up and fingers are numb. She sleeps poorly secondary to erratic scheduling that has led her to work night shift only to find her long lost circadian rhythm that has left her fatigued and staring at the ceiling contemplating, "Is this really what I signed up for?" She suffers from the dimming joy of patient care that is ruled by patient satisfaction surveys that seemingly supersede the long-preached standard of evidenced-based medicine that was engrained in her throughout medical school and residency. She is tired of writing for Z-packs and Amoxicillin to keep patients happy, so she can get that Press Ganey Score card just right even when she feels it goes against her values. She is also confused by her pay check monthly. I mean what in the hell is an RVU really? She is tired of feeling undervalued and monetized by a system of government bureaucracy that undercuts physicians and penalizes you for not knowing all the rules of a 10,000-page rule book. She does love medicine and service is embedded in her DNA. She wants to continue patient care in a more meaningful and caring way with the total care of the patient in mind. She also wants to nurture her passion for entrepreneurship and her love of music. She also wants to settle down and fulfill her goal of a loving and supportive marriage relationship and start a family.

O: Dr. Pinckney is happily unconventional, well-liked and loved by her friends, family and colleagues. Dr. Pinckney has been recently challenged by a contentious and false accusation of common law marriage that has plagued her finances, her energy and her time. Despite the economic and emotional drain, Dr. Pinckney is thriving in a positive and loving relationship. Dr. Pinckney has continued to thrive in her professional career through an evolution and transformation of her mindset through coaching, meditation and an education in business and entrepreneurship that has shifted her paradigm from just and employee to a business owner.

A: Dr. Pinckney is a full-time Emergency Physician Attending, Medical Director, girlfriend and lover of life, music, service and travel.

P: Dr. Pinckney has re-invented herself and branded herself as Dr Cwanza MD and DJ Dr Code Blue who continues to see patients in the emergency department, started a mobile physician and concierge service, an international and national DJ, lifestyle coach and founder of Alchemy Concierge, PLLC.

Dr. Cwanza's Story

"WTF?" No, seriously... "WTF?" As I am sitting down to write this chapter, I am sitting on a hard bench in a cold court room listening to flat out lies and allegations about me that make no sense. I'm not married... how many more times can I say that? I don't have a ring, no ceremony, no wedding cake, no proposal, no pictures..." How Sway..." Just How? Oh, and I forgot to mention this has been going on for about a year and a half. I have spent more money than I care to admit protecting myself from the ramifications of something I did not do. Now, I'm no saint but this one wasn't on me. I take accountability in that I wasn't the best girlfriend at the end and for sure could have handled that relationship with more respect and care, which has been a lesson for me to learn and grow from... and after a non-divorce divorce (completely made up word that describes a made up situation) you either shit and get off the pot and grow or you lay down. But I am not the laying down type. This is not a woe is me tale, this is a "Whoa... this is me" tale. You see, what I learned through this huge contrast is that we are a product of our choices and are external manifestations of how we choose to deal with the perceived contrasts and attracted blessings that meet us all along the journey of life. Now don't get me wrong, moving out of a house that I own to protect my interests, and moving in with my Mom and Dad was humbling for sure, but I learned something valuable; there is learning and joy in every experience. I learned that what was meant to break me actually birthed my true potential. What I perceived as probable professional embarrassment, an unloading of friends who didn't want to deal with drama, and the doomsday of telling a really fly person I wanted to date I stayed with my Mama was overwhelming to say the least. My days of balling out, doing whatever I wanted and living as an unashamed pleasure seeker came to a drastic halt. I realized that in order to become the person I always dreamed of becoming I needed to take accountability for my choices in life, forget the past, start looking forward and living in my truth. I decided that I was no longer the chick to lie down and take it and that I could persist and fight for my truth with integrity and inner strength. I for sure have had good and bad days and would be lying if I didn't cry and say, "Why, Lord?" But, instead of beating myself up when I felt bad I learned how to create tools to strengthen myself through working with a coach, letting go of shame, letting go of guilt and letting go of all of the stories that I believed about myself that were unintentionally planted in my subconscious. I learned that I am strong, smart, creative, powerful, unique, precious and genuinely loved by a great many people. I learned that I have the patience of Job and that I really didn't need all the fancy things I loved to surround myself with to be happy. I found real joy, inner joy, and passion to follow my truth and life vision. Now I could go on for days on my personal drama triad, but I don't live in that space except to help people learn from my experience. I wish no ill will on anyone and I certainly take accountability in all my choices that led to some chaos in my life and I have moved on from that. But sometimes it takes a major shakeup to wake your mind and spirit up.

So, let's get back to medicine. I love medicine. I love science. I love my patients. I just didn't love the way I was practicing medicine and that is a choice. So, I created something unique for me. I formed a very small concierge practice to care for patients when they need me in a place they feel comfortable. It's so cool to get to sit down and listen and teach and develop a treatment plan that is in line with what is medically sound, what works for the lifestyle of each patient, and teach and really explain the why, the importance and the goal for each individual patient outcome. I always envisioned a really close relationship with a small number of patients and watching them transform. I also jumped in and found my love for music again and started DJing. What started as a hobby has become a business. I have traveled to multiple countries; DJ'd events in multiple states and locally, and if you can believe it, I learned how to DJ by watching you tube. I have stepped it up now and work with an amazing DJ (shout out to DJ Shante) who has shared her gifts and passion and helped me to rapidly step up my game. You never stop learning and you never stop seeking those who know more and can show you better ways to progress in your passion. DJ DR Code Blue is a brand that is expanding into music production, mediation music, music therapy and education. My love for music turned into a #1 amazon bestselling book entitled *Music and Medicine Vol 1.* and I am so touched by all of the people who have told me that they read the book with their boyfriend because they love DJ Screw or Stevie Wonder, or that they were never interested in science, but they loved learning about the pathophysiology of the disease processes that plagued these amazing artists. There is something very special about crafting something out of love and having someone tell you they learned something new. I don't mean that in an ego-based way. I mean that in a confirmation of what the Lord and Universe put in my heart. Once I learned how to get out of my own way, really good things have been vibrating toward me. It's still work, but it's work that feels good. It feels inspired. It feels like a natural vibration and flow. I bounce to my own beat now and it is the best feeling ever. I mean of course as you start vibrating higher the proverbial "s-h-i-t" always gets flung your way, but when you take energy off of it and use it as opportunities to learn you can let the "s-h-i-t" fly because I find it doesn't really move me anymore. I really have opened my spirit to see the foolishness coming and then bobbing and weaving like Apollo Creed to get out the way before it hits me. Now I am not always fast enough, so when contrasting things come I just learn, avoid beating myself up and always look forward. I also found a love for coaching. The joy of sharing what I have learned about the laws of attraction, mindfulness, the peace that comes when you stop going against the grain and moving in the direction of what makes you feel good and alive has been nothing short of life-changing for me as much as my coaching clients. So, when I think about the idea of quitting medicine, it doesn't fit anymore, because the solution never lived within the problem. The solution for me was in deciding to no longer fight the challenging aspects of life and medicine, but to instead always seek to move away from uncomfortable contrast and align myself with the easy flow of my love for science, medicine, art, culture, travel, service and people within the same stream of consciousness. And that feels good. Now, I enjoy a lighter work schedule, a busy DJ business that is morphing into production and therapeutic modalities, I podcast, seek to inspire people on social media, have hit a national platform for the first time and am a best-selling author. Life is good and the challenges that arise are opportunities to grow and learn. So yeah, I'm sitting in court today when I could be resting but guess what? Instead of being angry, I am writing and sharing my story with all of you because it feels good and the universe is always working things out for me and I have faith in the word of God and his promises for my life.

I wake up every day with a goal of having a "Lovely Day" as Bill Withers penned his famous song. "Live my life like it's Golden," as Jill Scott so vibrantly sings about, and lay down at night, in the words of my favorite Ice Cube song saying to myself, "Today was a Good Day." So, as this year spins on, I am reaching higher and higher and trying to reach and serve as many people as I can to express my mantra, "Life is a turntable." Brothers and sisters, move to your own beat not anyone else's. If you don't like the song life is playing, re-mix it or change the record but just like the turntable, we always have to keep spinning forward.

Mani Saint Victor, MD

"There is a quiet inner voice that knows, in this moment, what is right for you. Tune in. Listen. Trust your intuition and be receptive and adaptive to the feedback."

Mani Saint Victor, MD

When you aren't where you want to be, a map can be a godsend. When you're headed in the wrong direction, your map can be a life sentence. My map to a seismic shift in lifestyle and circumstance from humble beginnings was medicine. It was the path to credibility and fulfillment and it led me to the nation's most respected university, past the milestones of marriage and family, through years of tightly prescribed study in medical school and into the badlands of middle age and its attendant responsibilities. Then it failed me.

2008 was the year my GPS got stuck on "recalculating route."

Suddenly "mapless," I was forced to reassess the destination a younger, less imaginative me typed in all those years ago. The lessons I earned--earned, not learned--through collaboration with gifted clinicians and thinkers have reshaped my life's work.

What if I could take my experience, compare it with those of what I now know to be innumerable highly-trained professionals and come up with strategies to help all kinds of people hold their maps accountable to their truest selves in the pursuit of work that leads to real and lasting fulfillment? A village of like-minded physicians and practitioners have shown me that I can.

I believe that hearing the call of one's true destination is a gift and the habit of taking action in service of that gift is a skill. The most important of these skills is the first step off of an expensively paved road in the wrong direction.

S: *45-year-old with a vision that burns inside of him now more than ever*

O: *In the final stages of putting together volume 2 of what was once a crazy dream and idea that Doc Nicole Swiner and I shared.*

A: *Holding steady after a challenging yet transformative year. Closer to my truth now than ever.*

P: *Let's. Get. It.*

Dr. Saint Victor's Story

I don't know.

That's the simple truth that has become the source of so much equanimity for me. It has opened me up to so much abundance that I can't begin to tell you. I spent my medical life so afraid that someone would reveal a crack in my armor, expose some flaw and humiliate me publicly that it controlled my life.

Too many of my decisions and actions were based on the need to look and act like a doctor and look successful. Even after I left medicine in 2008 and joined a virtual world startup, it continued. Having been trained in an environment where each of my mistakes felt amplified to the point of life and death (yeah, I get it; often they literally were-- yep... got it).

So, when Nicole and I sat down here at Busboys and Poets in DC to write our chapters, my first response...

I don't know.

I didn't know that all of you would show up and share your stories with me, revealing how you were being mistreated in your clinics and that every attempt to request change was being interpreted as a lack of dedication to medicine. I didn't know that you would come through in droves when I had my heart attack and landed in the ICU for a couple of days and in the hospital for 3 weeks. I didn't know that so many of you had done such amazing and inspiring things with your degrees. You made medicine yours! Respect!!!

But now I know that I don't know.

As I write this brief chapter, I'm humbled by the depth of expression and vulnerability that the physician-authors joining us for this journey have braved. I don't know how each of their stories will enhance your life and inspire you to dig deeper and live more meaningfully.

Ironically, it's accepting not knowing that has set me free. Those of you who have known me since my Harvard pre-med days know that I am super-obsessed with empirics. Being that I'm a bit of a neurotic at the core, I long had a desperate need to nourish my illusion of control. Those of you who knew me in med school, when I re-ignited my fixation with software and artificial intelligence, remember that I was convinced that all reality could be reduced to a formula. This last year and some months have been about moving beyond that.

Accepting the unknown as a scientist means maintaining my intellectual curiosity while maintaining my sanity. I had to not only let go of the paralyzing perfectionist skeptic in me but also learn to trust. Trust came with giving myself permission to be human and make mistakes. Beyond that, it came with realizing that there are many things that can't be neatly put into the right or wrong/good or bad basket. Strangely, all this self-compassion freed me to see and accept people as they are. It also opened me up to understanding a different paradigm of science that includes me, my feelings, my needs, my desires, and my fears.

Some of you may remember that I was three days into the third year of my psychiatry residency before I quit medicine for the third time. The first question I get from other docs is, "Why?" Next, like clockwork, I'll get, "You were so close to finishing." Then, in many cases, I can see them processing, searching for what was wrong with me, why I wasn't cut out for medicine. That used to wound me deeply because the conversation that followed was rarely about why I made the decision to pursue a life about medicine and more about defending *their* worldview of medicine as the ultimate... medicine.

Keep in mind that I talk to hundreds of people a month about this topic now. It took me hundreds of these discussions to come to the realization that my answer had to be vulnerable, true, and meaningful. It took me longer to realize that, among the majority of people, it would fall on deaf ears. They are not ready to hear it yet. It sounds like gibberish.

It has been 10 years since I resigned from my psychiatry residency now. The questions I get now have morphed. The most honest question I get is, "Do you regret leaving?" Yes and no.

Looking back now on my journey through entrepreneurship, I can say, "Eh, sorta." I don't regret *that* I left. I regret *how* I left. I was ashamed and felt like a failure for not completing what I set out to do as a teenager. I've never been a quitter. Even the word "quit" does something limbic and visceral to me. I imagine how life would have been different had I finished my residency and had a psychiatrist's salary to power my business. Also, there's the aspect of being limited (if only in my mind) by not having fully immersed myself in the circle of my peers such that I have that deep relationship with them that traversing adversity affords. A lot of my lifelong med friends feel as if I betrayed them when I went on the paper cha$e.

It's challenging for me to explain that though the money offered to me by the startup legitimized my decision to switch careers, I was in a pain that was calling me to dig deeper and do things that looked dumb on the surface.

Years later, I have reconciled a lot of the wounds from my journey through medical training, a lot of the healing and looking back through the lens of personal responsibility for my life outcomes.   The times when I didn't speak my desires, when I chose to people-please, when I took shortcuts instead of developing a deeper discipline from within--until I look at where I am now and what my path has allowed me to do. I'm honored that so many doctors come to me when they need someone to talk to. Whether it's for a quick drop-by sanity check or to think through some strategies, or to get through a tough life event, my clients turn to me and trust me. They know that I've traveled the medical road with them, and I won't judge. I've been through too much of it myself- he who lives in a glass house...

The best place to reach me if you'd like to follow my journey is on my website <u>manisaintvictormd.com</u>. Reach out to me when you're ready to make the most of your own journey. I'm looking forward to seeing what we can accomplish together.

Rae Smith-Peart, MD

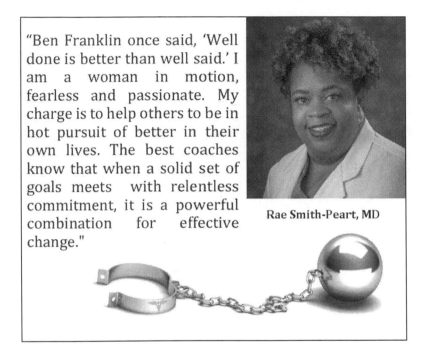

"Ben Franklin once said, 'Well done is better than well said.' I am a woman in motion, fearless and passionate. My charge is to help others to be in hot pursuit of better in their own lives. The best coaches know that when a solid set of goals meets with relentless commitment, it is a powerful combination for effective change."

Rae Smith-Peart, MD

Dr. Rae Smith is a community pediatrician with emphasis in pediatric emergency medicine and pediatric hospital care. She started her medical career as a registered pharmacist, having had the opportunity to work both independent retail and hospital-based pharmacy.

She then went on to complete her medical degree at Tulane University in her proclaimed hometown, New Orleans, LA. After medical school, she trained and finished her pediatric residency in Dallas at University of Texas-Southwestern. That training gave her a solid foundation for her dynamic medical practice that she enjoys today.

If you have ever wanted better health especially after a major health crisis or after the shock of a loved one's illness, then you know what drives Dr. Rae's health vision. Having a child at an older age, after a battle with infertility, she realized the tangible importance of being an advocate and participant in your own health care.

She is a thriving breast cancer survivor. This major life event was a reinforcement that health is a daily decision and how crucial proper, quality nutritional supplements can be. Frankly, they can be the difference between life and death.

She is a proponent of holistic self-care through her unique and dynamic health coaching and plant based nutritional supplementation.

Now, she and her phenomenal husband have set out on a new endeavor to address fresh produce disparity in inner city areas. As well, they are launching unique systems that will "green up" large organizations and schools, which will have a positive impact on our future generations.

She looks forward to connecting with you. Please find her on all social media and www.DrRaeSmithMD.

S: 40-something female who is awakening to an alternative reality in her medical career.

O: In moderate distress, she is obviously straining for new life and desperately sought-after professional satisfaction

A: Depleted and disillusioned idealist physician

P: Transfuse with a new medical pathway, also this subject will need to open her eyes to more than medicine

Dr. Smith-Peart's Story

I was born to a young ambitious couple; Henry and Brenda Smith. My father was career military with a distinguished and exemplary career. I learned from my father that family is first. My dad was and is a very intelligent man. He is a history buff like I have never seen. He always told me about our ancestral history. Due to his influence, I grew up knowing who I am and what I was capable of. His offbeat sense of humor, diligence and charisma are like magic to his daughter.

My mom is, as I quote "one of the smartest people that I have ever met," an enigma. She grew up in a small community; she then relocated to a metropolitan area. She was purported to hate the sight of anyone's blood, yet she became one of the best nurses in this large metropolitan medical facility. She grew up with her father and mother, in an intact family. Brenda is a woman with a strained back story. I learned from my mother to rely on my faith and hard work; everything else is a possible disappointment.

I am both right and left-brained, depending on the situation. A chameleon. I have always had an appreciation for literature and the arts. At seven years old, I had a poem published in a nationally circulated children's magazine. I remember that poem by heart even to this day.

Adjectives that describe me--Different. Odd. Only. These are the words that I knew early on in life.

As far as the left brain, I had a photographic memory, even though I did not know exactly what that meant. I figured that everyone's brain worked that way until the later health events let me know that this was not true.

Academia has always been my strong suit. I excelled, although some teachers did not believe that this little black girl could be so smart. Still, I easily succeeded in this arena. I won student awards and a few teachers' respect. It was almost idyllic.

The flip side of that coin was that I have always felt a certain disconnect with people my age, my peers. I am an only child, so I did not grow up around other kids. I was always social. I made associates easily, no difficulty there. However, that did not translate to sleepovers or hanging out.

I have always felt a certain level of isolation. Trust me. It is part of my individual journey, so there is no remorse, just a point of reflection. At the core of it, I am an introvert. An outgoing introvert, but an introvert nonetheless.

As school progressed, I noticed an intrapersonal divide. This happens most commonly with other black classmates. I was even called "Oreo" at one point. Thank goodness, it did not become a popular nickname. That moniker confused me because I have always known my identity. Due to my demeanor, other black students did not find it credible that I was indeed comfortable in my full self.

As most of my peers went to parties and "enjoyed life," I sequestered myself in true "bookworm" fashion. So, the invitations disappeared, as did most of my social life. I felt like the princess in the tower, although I do not claim that narrative. Princesses always seem to be waiting, at least back in the day. This "princess" was far too proactive for that.

I continued to excel scholastically until high school. There, I found my first academic challenges, despite being around odd, different students like myself. All the kids were intelligent, not just me. So, it was a whole new ball game. There was more diversity, which was both refreshing and alarming. During my high school years, I was accepted to a performing arts school for singing. However, I declined the invitation. I did not want to do the additional work; I was already struggling in high school. Although I did very well in Spanish, everything else was strenuous.

I was accepted to a minority-based science summer program before college. That was before the days of

STEM. This greatly changed the trajectory of my future. Under the guidance of my project supervisor, I applied to pharmacy school. I graduated with honors with my Bachelor's in Pharmacy, which was unusual for an African-American student despite having attended an HBCU.

When I was accepted to medical school, I was ecstatic. It was my first-choice school. When I went on the interview, all went well until the cadaver lab visit. No, I did not get queasy. I probably could not recreate this scenario even if I tried. The floor was slightly elevated. I stepped into the lab wearing low heels, one of those shoes caught the lip of the tile and went skidding all the way across the floor. I just knew at that point that my dream of going to my number one choice was gone. However, when I got that acceptance letter in my parents' mailbox, it was pure celebration.

While in medical school, I was able to pursue my passion of writing. My dean, who is one of the most generous people I have ever known, was supportive of our student body. I was able to get a literary journal published and exhibit others' works of art at our school. It was glorious. I remembered my early childhood when I wrote my first poem. During that same seven-year-old phase, I knew that I wanted to be a pediatrician. So, it was a juxtaposition of my purpose and passion all in one moment.

At the end of my medical school career, I matched to my first-choice residency program. It was in Dallas. It would be the first time that I would be away from home for a period of time. The butterfly had finally reached the capacity of the chrysalis. This independence experience was so necessary. Often, it is an unspoken concern that when you get on your own, you will get "buck wild." Well, I have never been that exciting. Boring. I know. Still, it was a time of self-discovery and expansion.

I have always thought of my life as sheltered and magical. Until August 2002. I had married my best friend that previous October. Since I married later in life, we needed to get busy with "making some babies." I stopped my birth control in February and we got pregnant that month.

August 2002, I had my first miscarriage. It would prove to be the first of several. Six to be exact. The infertility game began in earnest. It is not a game that you want to play. What choice did we have? I had the tests, so many tests. Since I had been pregnant several times, my husband did not have any testing to do. After all, he has 17 siblings in all. Yup. Seventeen. We, as a couple, didn't have a problem getting pregnant. As evidenced by the six miscarriages, or spontaneous abortions in medical terminology. However, with the ease of getting pregnant, I was having a challenge of "staying" pregnant. So, I had genetic testing, both on myself and the fetuses. Normal. Tests on my reproductive system. Talking about feeling vulnerable. When all you want is to have a baby, and then you have to discover if you are adequate in the "woman" department. A lot of women go through this. I am not the only one. In the specialist's words, I had the "eggs of a teenager." So, what was the problem? We finally found the reason. I had heavy periods from an early age. I often complained to my pediatrician and later the gynecologist. Never was I directed to seek further testing. I would have found out that I had fibroids, endometriosis and a bicornuate uterus. Even though it is not a common cause, I had a fibroid in a position that prevented the fetus from attaching to the needed blood supply. Despite the numerous ultrasounds in early pregnancy, there was never a heartbeat. I went to another specialist and decided to have both a fibromyectomy and endometrial ablation. Ten months later, we had our beautiful rainbow baby.

Some may wonder if I was ever bitter for mothers of newborns that I had to care for. I never was. I was elated for them. What it did change in me was my "tolerance" for those who abuse children. Knowing that I wanted a baby so desperately and there were other families or guardians who were intentionally harming theirs incensed me.

When I was diagnosed with right-sided stage 2 breast cancer in December 2010, I had a two-year-old at the time. I was overwhelmed. At the time, I was told the lump that I found was likely benign. Ladies and gentlemen, I cannot stress enough--be proactive in your health. I insisted that the entire lump be removed. It was fortunate that I had the insight to insist on that. You do not have to be a medical professional to be your own health and wellness advocate. I maintained respect for myself and my care team in the process.

I decided to have chemotherapy and radiation, since the surgery had already been done.

I went through breast surgery, port placement and chemotherapy easily; if easy is a term that anyone uses regarding cancer treatment. As I mentioned, my mom is a nurse. While I really liked my physicians, those nurses told me the insider's knowledge. One of my chemotherapy agents was red, absolutely red. When it would infuse, I could taste it. I have never experienced anything like that before. It tasted like rancid metal. The trick was to chew bubble gum to keep that putrid taste at bay. I always went to the infusion suite with a pack of sugar free gum. Word to the wise. Also, my rainbow baby was a toddler at the time. One of my favorite infusion nurses said, "Honey, I know that you have a little one at home. Be sure to keep your baby out of the bathroom that you use until your urine is not red like this medicine." It got real at that moment. I thought that the cancer diagnosis was a gut punch. This statement took my breath away. To think that something in the treatment that I was counting on to eradicate this cancer could be transferred to my child was frightening. I committed to being more vigilant about caring for both myself and my family. When treatment was finished, I had gone through yet another metamorphosis. You have these images in your head of what a cancer patient looks like. Painfully thin. Dark, bleak circles under the eyes. Bald head. I am sure that some go through this. I had one of the three- Grace Jones style. I miss my bald head sometimes. The fact that I looked like everyone else was a two-edged blade. It definitely cut both ways. I was overjoyed that I had survived this treatment. My medical oncologist told me, "You got some strong bone marrow!" I was thankful. In the same respect, I think that helped both me and those around me deflect the gravity of the situation. Although I did not look worse for wear on the outside, I was a crumbling mess on the inside. That soon became undeniably evident in a short period of time. My blood pressure was elevated, and my blood sugars were too high--a culmination of genetics and all the steroids. My mood was erratic. Once again, thanks to the steroids. My energy was poor. I was waking up tired and going to bed absolutely exhausted. I was suffering from thick brain fog. That was not going to work, neither figuratively nor literally. I have had eczema since childhood, but these skin rashes were out of control. I thought that the cancer was all that I needed to consider. That was only the beginning. I needed to recover my health. I was on a quest. Thankfully, that quest resulted in my better health, even better than pre-diagnosis.

The recovery in my health has been amazing, a huge blessing. I uncovered a system of health and wellness products that was pivotal in my optimal health. I got my mojo back. I have gone down eight dress sizes and feel better than I ever have. I promote these tools over social media and in my everyday life. As a physician and pharmacist, I know that people often are suffering with one thing or another, health-wise. Unfortunately, we are implementing band aids when there is a gaping wound. Also, I have the distinct honor of being a business coach and supporting others in their dreams.

I work within both my local and global community. The best thing that anyone can do is to be of service to someone else, whether that is a little gesture or huge transformation.

So, the big C changed my life. Not cancer, though. Compassion.

C. Nicole Swiner, MD

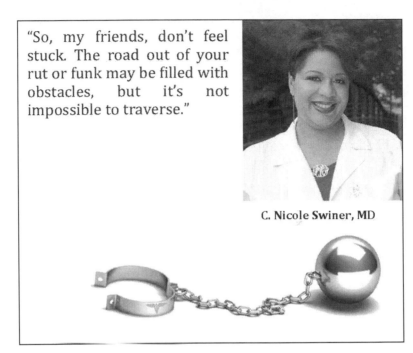

"So, my friends, don't feel stuck. The road out of your rut or funk may be filled with obstacles, but it's not impossible to traverse."

C. Nicole Swiner, MD

Voted 1 of 10 Best Doctors in NC in 2017, DocSwiner is a family physician, two-time best-selling author, blogger, speaker, wife and mother in Durham. She is also affectionately known as the *Superwoman Complex* expert and has written two best-selling books on the topic. She loves taking care of the family as a whole—from the cradle to the grave. Her interests include minority health, women's health, self-care and entrepreneurship. She attended Duke University and went to medical school at the Medical University of South Carolina in Charleston, SC. She's lived in the Triangle (Durham, NC) since finishing residency at UNC-Chapel Hill and continues teaching as an Adjunct Associate Professor with the Family Medicine department. When she's not treating patients at Durham Family Medicine, she's speaking locally and nationally, blogging, teaching others to self-publish and spending time with her family. Her passion is making medicine "plain" to her patients, so that all people, from all walks of life, can understand how to take better care of themselves and their families. She often blogs, guest blogs and speaks locally and nationally on these and other topics. She is also available as an influencer and brand ambassador, as she's previously represented SheBuysCars, Hyundai, prAna clothing, DurhamKnows HIV awareness and Scarlet Myth

Cosmetics. Contact her at cnswiner@gmail.com for further information.

S: 40-year-old (still) full-time doc, publisher, speaker & consultant, continuing to seek joy and balance in work, family and love.

O: Happy, yet not settling for contentment. Still working on "baby" weight five years later, but unashamedly enjoying good food and wine. All faculties secure and intact.

A: Superwoman (#nosuperwoman) in full effect

P: Has given up on the myth of work-life balance, and now will work on more work-life integration. Here's how:

DocSwiner's Story

I turned 40 this year, thank God. Leading up to this milestone birthday, I wondered what kind of emotional and mental changes I'd experience. Nothing much changed, except for my tolerance and patience, a bit. I now know what I want out of life and work, and I'll fight my hardest to achieve.

Today, as I write, on 7/23/18 at 4pm, two (a mother and daughter pair) of my most challenging patients "let me have it." They've noticed that I'm no longer in clinic on Mondays and Fridays, and on days that I am here, I've included some telemedicine slots with my clinic appointments. The elderly mother is none-too-pleased, as she mentions that I should have "thought about that before I went to medical school, if you wanted to work less and take more time off." Two or three years ago, this would have upset me at the thought that she felt I should let my career and patients control me and my happiness in this way. Today, I laughed to myself and to her middle –aged daughter, who looked at me apologetically and was horrified that her mother would talk to me in such a way. I patted the daughter's knee and reassured her that I was ok with it, and just said I was "unbothered." The truth is, I understand and understood where the mother is coming from—she's used to the old fashioned doctor (and, the old fashioned me) that was at her every beckoning call, would freely work her into the schedule whenever she needed and drop all things to make her happy, even while she was being belligerent to me and the staff at times. The new practicing physician in me now knows that I'm worth more than that.

I'm not going to explain to every one of my patients (I will to some if asked in the right fashion) why I'm making the decision to cut back to three days a week in clinic and work from the home the other two; but I will explain to you. As I finish this chapter, sitting next to my co-founder, Mani, on a Friday morning, in DC at Busboys and Poets (a restaurant and bar I've always wanted to come to), I feel blessed. I'm trying to create a lifestyle and career in which I can work remotely. My kids are now in Kindergarten and second grade, and I'd love to be home more for them and go on some field trips. I'm loving the career consulting and publishing work I've been doing for the past three years, and I want to be more free to travel to speak and meet clients. The next step may be to become licensed in other states, so I'm able to do telemedicine visits even when I'm on the road. I think the options are endless.

So, my friends, don't feel stuck. The road of out your rut or funk may be filled with obstacles, but it's not impossible to traverse. If you need help—emotional, mental, financial, strategic—then don't be afraid to reach out to mentors and experts. Create the work-life balance and integration that you desire.

LaKesha M Davison, MD

Editor

LaKesha comes by her proclivity for editing honestly. Since her early childhood, she has always been fascinated with words. In elementary school, she was spelling bee champion and proudly went on to represent her school at the regional championship. She continues to be a voracious reader with diverse tastes, although young adult and fantasy literature hold a special place in her heart. Alongside band, she started studying Spanish in junior high (because why limit yourself to reading in one language when you can do so in two?) and even developed a reputation for enjoying proofreading others' work. She continued her studies in Florida State University, graduating with a double major in Biology and Spanish and a minor in linguistics. In an attempt to match her spelling bee achievement, she nabbed a scholarship for having the highest grade in Spanish in the entire department!

After FSU, LaKesha pursued her medical studies in Emory University School of Medicine. She enjoyed Atlanta so much she decided to stick around for pediatric residency at Emory with an extra year as a Chief Resident. Since then, she has been loving on the children of Atlanta as a general pediatrician with some stints in medical missions abroad in Thailand and Jamaica. She is passionate about advocating for families, helping teens take ownership of their health, and educating children to make healthy choices to combat obesity.

In her spare time, you'll find LaKesha perfecting her running PR, sweating in spin class, or curating an outfit for the next DragonCon. She hopes to continue expanding her editing work and is currently a reviewer of board style questions for pediatric residents and offers proofreading/copyediting services for several entrepreneurs' blog posts.

Afterword

So how are you feeling now?

That was quite a ride, eh?

We're honored that you invested the time in exploring our stories and your own ideas in this second journey. Take some time to sit with the feelings that our physician authors evoked in you. Don't just keep doing what was grinding you down before. Check in with yourself from time to time to assess how you're growing from these new perspectives. Notice which of our authors you identify with the most and reach out to them. They're waiting for you to connect to share your story.

As a matter of fact, there is a whole universe of physicians waiting for you to share your story. Get to writing it into reality. When you hit a stuck point, when you're doubting yourself, when adversity and discouragement seem to be rearing their heads to block your destiny, remember that this is the growth that is preparing you to reach your full potential.

Your unique path, with all its trials and tribulations, is the road to connecting with your special gifts. Within the uncertainty awaits your opportunity to make your contribution and have a lasting impact.

On behalf of our physician authors, I welcome you to the other side. Enjoy the view, clarity, and confidence that emerges from having the courage to explore Thinking About Quitting Medicine.

Until volume 3!

28782492R00090

Made in the USA
Columbia, SC
17 October 2018